The Story of a Hedge School Master

The Story of a HEDGE SCHOOL MASTER

Eugene Watters

being the Life and Adventures of
a Maker of Men
of 200 Years ago
distilled from the exploits
of many nameless men
and dedicated
to Teachers everywhere

MERCIER EDUCATIONAL
Cork and Dublin

The Mercier Press Limited
4 Bridge Street, Cork
25 Lower Abbey Street, Dublin 1

The Story of a Hedge School Master
ISBN 0 85342 436 5

Cover design: Alan Phelan

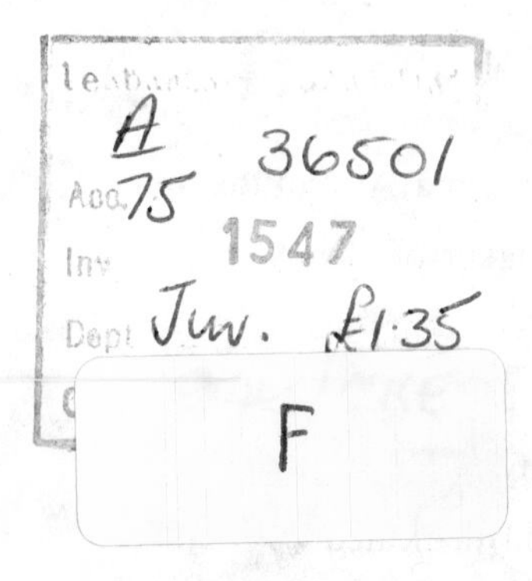

Printed in the Republic of Ireland

CONTENTS

The Dangerous Gift

THE STORY BEGINS near the village of Aughrim in Co. Galway where Tadhgeen Kelly, a herd on the land of Archdeacon Trench, had his cabin and family of twelve or fifteen boys and girls. Only his wife knew exactly how many, for the biggest boys were away shouldering their spades to the hiring-fairs beyond the Shannon, and a couple of the girls were out at service, while the smallest were still crawling naked in the mud on the floor. Owen was one of the youngest of them, sleeping warm with a batch of brothers and sisters in the loft above the fire-place, where they shared the straw with the roosting hens.

He was a sturdy little fellow, well able to fight his corner in the crowded cabin and get his share of the steaming pot of potatoes which his mother placed in the centre of the floor for all her little half-naked family to sit around and eat. They were among the poorest of the poor, and were called the Poreen Kellys because they ate the 'poreens' or tiny potatoes which other families kept for the pig.

At the age of seven, still wearing petticoats and with an old cap of his father's pushed down on his tangled mop of tawny hair, he was able to go on his own into the village where Mr.

McEntaggart the Cobbler had his cottage, nicely whitewashed and with diamond panes of glass. The Cobbler took a liking to him for he was always asking questions — what's this for? what's that for? Why have you a wooden leg? was it fighting? and why does Mr. Trench have a woman-wife and the Priest have none? The Cobbler used to give him parcels of brogues he had made or mended, shoes, riding-boots, saddles even, to deliver to the customers, warning him to bring the articles back if he didn't get the money.

At night in the warm nest above the fireplace he would keep his brothers and sisters awake for hours, telling them of the strange places and the strange people there were in the world. In a babble of words he would bring them by fairy thorns and wild-apple hedgerows to cabin doors, where a woman would come out wearing boots like a man; or scutting on the shafts of a cart down breakneck boreens to farmyards and big kitchens full of giant pots of meat, and up forbidden avenues to 'Gintry Houses,' and once the whole three miles to Garbally Court itself and into the yard, where he saw foxhounds and the Earl's daughters, all diamonds and feathers in their hair, sitting with knees crossed sideways on horses as high as a house. And his voice would change according to the people he was talking about, and he could even speak like the gentry.

The father and mother by the hearth below, listening, crossed themselves and said, 'That child is not right.'

It wasn't long till he was known far and wide as the Cobbler's Oweneen. One night having done his errands it was later than usual when he returned to the Cobbler's house. He found the old man by the fireside, the oil-lamp lit close to his elbow, an immense book open and his spectacles bent close to the page. Oweneen gazed mouth-open at a picture of a boy in petticoats and a huge man in an iron shirt and horns on his head, standing half-way to the sky.

'Is that a Giant, sir?'

'Oh,' said the Cobbler, 'are you back?'

'Yessir. Who's that little boy?'

'That's King David when he was a wee fella.'

'Is he the "Prodestung" King of England, sir?'

'Ah dear no. David is dead these few thousand years.'

'Then how d'you know it's him?'

'Because the book tells me. It talks to me, silent.'

'Is it . . . magicky?'

'Yes boy, it's magic. It's also called reading.'

'Could I hear it talking, sir, d'you think?'

'See those marks on the paper? Well, every

little bundle of marks is a word. Listen.' And with that the old man began to move his finger along the marks and talk the words, how David was a poor boy herding sheep in the hills, but all unbeknown he was a King, and he let fly with a stone out of his sling and knocked the Giant Goliath flat on his back.

The boy stared at the book, his brow puckered. 'Could I make it talk like that?'

'You could, avic. But you'd have to learn.'

'Would you learn me?'

The Cobbler put his hand on the boy's head, pushed the tousled hair from his small bright eyes. 'Oweneen of the O'Kellys, me lad, you ask for a terrible gift. The man that learns to read this book is marked for life. He'll grow a stranger to his own people, a stranger to the world of men and markets and the mud of the fields. And the more he knows the more his heart will hunger to know, and he'll earn many an empty day, many a hard knock and a cut head, until he goes down a lonely old man into an unmarked grave. Think twice before you ask for such a dangerous gift.'

'Learn me, sir,' said the boy.

'In the Lord's name, then so be it.' He went to the bench, took a piece of chalk and a bit of sole-leather. 'Now here's where we start. This is the letter A . . .'

Past midnight, going barefoot home across the frozen fields, he felt no cold, the new letters marched across the sky before his eyes among the stars.

He Learns the Law

DURING THE NEXT seven or eight years, there where that long low Hill of Aughrim with its dark memories lies along the road to Galway and the Western Sea, the Cobbler's Oweneen learned many things. He learned to use the awl and the knife, cut out a pair of soles, drive wooden pegs, stitch a bit of harness leather or put a neat toe-cap on a lady's boot. 'No man that can set his hands to a craft need starve,' said the Cobbler.

He learned to write, add shillings and pence, keep accounts, first on a bit of slate till he had mastered the mystery, then with a quill pen on paper. He copied the Cobbler's style, put fine flourishes to the capital letters in the bills he made out for saddle-girths and brogues. The Cobbler was a hard taskmaster, and it was years before he would let Oweneen write a bill for the Archdeacon, or for the Steward at Garbally Court.

It became clear to him that apart from his own people, the Poreen Kellys, Kellys of the Hill, Kellys of the Gripe, the Bummer Kellys, the

Informers, the Turfmould Kellys, the Patcheens, Kellys of the Stone House . . . there was a completely different class of humanity in the land. These were the Protestants or, as the Cobbler called them, the Williamites. He used to have a kind of pity for them, for the general feeling was that they were all damned.

The odd thing was that these poor benighted King Billyites seemed to have the best of it in food and clothes and fine horses; they owned the cornfields and the flocks and paid the wages; you had to touch your cap to them, and when you delivered them a bit of leatherwork they said, 'Thank you, boy,' without even a bit of a blessing or a humorous remark in the tail of their talk.

One day in the yard of the Earl's Court, he came upon a couple of Billyite boys of his own age, with books in their hands. Surprised, he asked, 'Are you fellas able to read?'

'Course we are.'

'Who learned you?'

They pointed up the stairs to the stable loft and said, 'In school.'

'What's school?'

They laughed, called him a poor little bog-trotter, and ran off calling in mockery, 'What's school? What's school?' He picked up a stone . . . let it drop again.

Back at the Cobbler's bench with a knife in his hand, he asked, 'Why can't we have a school?'

The Cobbler pointed with the handle of his awl through the open window at the green slopes of the Hill. 'That's the why,' he said briefly.

He went on stitching in silence, then the words broke from him as if they had been long suppressed. 'It was a Sunday, the 12th of July in the year 1691. I was a lad of 21 or 22, a trooper in Sarsfield's Horse, under the combined banners of France and the Catholic King James. There on that memorable Hill we met them — Dutch, Danes, Huguenots, Germans, English and Walloons — the half of Europe, under the banners of the Protestant Prince of Orange claiming to be King of England, Ireland, Scotland and Wales. They won the day. They now sit in the Parliament of Dublin and make the Laws.'

'What's the Laws?'

'How you must behave, or else you'll be brought before the Magistrates and fined, or jailed, or shipped away to the West Indies, according to the humour their Honours are in. And one of the Laws is that no Catholic may teach a school, or send his child to a school, or give lodgings to a schoolmaster.'

'But why?'

'They plan to make us an ignorant people, so that we may never rise up in arms against them again. A nation of bogtrotters, herds, stable-boys and kitchen-maids. A race of slaves — as they have made of the Red Indian nations in America — born in ignorance and reared in stupidity, that will touch their caps to the Conqueror and his Wife as if they were superior beings. Superior? huh, when we let them have the full shock of our charge across the Flanders fields of Oudenarde, they could feel then who was superior! Come here, boy.' He took down a heavy volume from his shelves. 'Here is a book for you that will go well with what you have read already of the ancient histories of Greece and Rome.' It was Count O'Kelly's 'History of Ireland.'

A new world was opened now to Oweneen's imagination. And a new idea: The Irish. His own ragged people, but curiously changed as if they had been turned by magic into kings and queens and soldiers and bishops and book-makers, chariot-fighting, feasting, building Monasteries bigger and more beautiful than the Protestant Church, discovering America, and playing wonderful music on the harp.

At home his family listened to him fascinated as he talked of 'The Irish.' His father and mother grew fearful: if that kind of talk got round to the Archdeacon's ears, they might all find themselves on the road — without a roof over their heads. 'And what's more,' he said, his voice rising, 'it was us Irish taught the English and the Protestants and them Europes when they didn't know B from a bull's foot!' 'Easy, boy, easy — many a man found himself lodged in Galway Jail for saying less than that.'

At times he felt himself growing apart from his family, their ideas and the way they looked at things. Yet he was deeply gripped by the intense affection that bound them all together.

But at times he was shaken with a fierce unrest that frightened him, a choking feeling for the light and the ideas that had been revealed to him in the printed page. A fit of anger would sweep over him, a hatred of their ragged clothes, their ragged English, his mother's bare feet on the earthen floor. He began to spend nearly all his time at the Cobbler's, at the bench or at the books. By the fire after the day's work, the old man drinking a glass of hot porter would speak of things he had locked away in his memory — the strange lands he had seen, the spires and the fortifications, the battles he had been in . . .

The old man drew maps — France, Austria, Spain, Naples, Savoy, Italy, the Papal States — there the Catholics were in power; there they were honoured and famous, in the Army, the Navy, the Revenue, the Universities, and in the Church. There the Irish were still 'The Irish.' But above all they were famous in France, 'Les Irlandais,' under the banners of King Louis charging the old Williamite enemy as the Irish Brigade.

'Could I go, sir?'

There was a long silence. 'First, you would have to go to school.'

'But, sir . . . sure we have no school?'

The old soldier took his tankard from the hob and sipped it silently, thinking.

One day in spring when the furze-buds were breaking in gold the Cobbler said to him, 'Owen, your time is come. Here is a yard-and-a-half of Belfast linen, start making yourself a pack for the road.'

It was into May before he was ready. The Cobbler laid out £5 on his equipment. He packed a few quires of foolscap paper, half a dozen Dutch quills, a couple of Histories, a Book-keeping ledger with the Rules of Arithmetic on the cover, a British Naval Almanac of the Tides and Times, a tattered Dictionary of French, cheese, oatcakes, an old wine-bottle filled with buttermilk, a spare shirt of good Holland cloth, two pairs of knitted socks, and a horse blanket. Besides his new pack, he was also to take the big shoulder-satchel in which he used to deliver the boots. This the Cobbler filled with a quarter-bend of sole leather, a few rolls of kip for repairing uppers, wax, balls of linen thread and pig-bristle needles, a knife, peg-awl and stitching-awl, hammer and a fold-up wooden last. He sewed two guineas in gold into the tail of his shirt, and gave him 30 shillings in silver to carry in the depth of his pocket.

'Tell no one your business,' he said. 'It is too dangerous. Go now to your father's house and say good-bye. Tell them you are going as a journeyman cobbler into the land beyond the Shannon, and will be away for the whole summer.'

Only his mother and a couple of the smaller ones were at home when he entered. His mother took one look at him, wrapped her arms about him and wailed like a wounded animal. He felt his heart would surely break; he had to force his legs to move across the threshold into the open air. Two of the little things came with him to the break in the whitethorns. He gave them a silver shilling each. Alone, he crawled into a clump of furze and rolled on the ground in agony.

The Cobbler awaited him, apron off, his best blue jacket on, white neckerchief, standing his full height. The book they had read the first night of all, lay open on the table, a sentence marked: 'Go out of thy Father's house and into the land which I shall show thee.'

'Here is a letter to Quartermaster Byrne. You will find him somewhere in the country beyond the Shannonwater, Protestant country, where he teaches the learned languages.'

'Yessir.'

The old man began to fidget, wiped his glasses, added another ball of thread to the satchel. Suddenly he said in a rough voice, 'Good-bye, O'Kelly. Go with God.'

Unable to speak, the boy found himself in the street. He looked back, saw the door shut, the diamond windows of the little house, the outline of the Hill darkening with rain. He put on his hareskin cap, set his face to the road.

Lissoy

SHANNONWATER FLOWED wide and bright beneath him as he walked in a daze across the Bridge of Athlone. He could almost see before him the Dutch gunners and the Williamites storming the Bridge as in the Cobbler's tale. Connacht behind him, ahead lay the grey and terrifying unknown — Kingbillyland.

At first sight there was not much difference — the same mud cabins, the Great House gates, corn ripening, the familiar furze in bloom, the same swarms of beggars on the roads. He had learned to fear the beggars more than the hard-hatted men on stout Williamite horses; he had cut himself a stout ash cudgel, and now carried his long knife hanging naked from his belt, as a warning. At 15, he was tall and wiry; his tawny hair uncut hung down to his shoulders. He took long strides like a man along the road into the new country, though inwardly he felt like a rabbit among savage hounds.

He slept that night at a roadside tavern, keeping his pack of books under his head and the knife under the blanket ready to his hand. Next morning he put on his sharpest voice and ordered a mug of beer and a slice of bread and ham. The woman cut it thick and plentiful. When he went to pay she pushed the coins back in his pocket. 'You're welcome, alanna, to the bed and the bite, for it's easy seen you're one of "them." Sure no son of a shoemaker ever walked and talked the way you do.'

He did a few jobs for her repairing corn-sacks and leather hinges on the doors. She took him into the kitchen and filled his bottle with new milk. But still he was afraid to ask her if she knew where Quartermaster Byrne lived, for fear she might be an Informer.

He walked off with a slouch, his head down, touched his forelock to the Gentry he met, and practised answering the beggars in the ragged English of the roads. He mended a bit of harness leather for a travelling tinman, who offered him a lift in his little covered cart in payment. 'It's on me way I am to do a few jobeens for Quartermaster Byrne,' he said boldly to the tinman.

'Arrah, Tomasheen Byrne, the baldy ould reprobate! Devil's skewer to him, and him in the Redcoats shooting at our decent Irish boys when he was overseas. Up at Lissoy he is, a-teaching of a 'Prodestung' skewel. Sure I'll lave you within an inch of his durestep.'

IT WAS DUSK when he knocked on the half-door. A roar bade him enter. A dread figure sat in the firelight, a great skull bald to the ears, a bush of moustache and sidewhiskers, in shirt-sleeves, glass of grog at his elbow. Trembling, Owen gave him the letter. He lit a candle, read and began in a quiet voice to curse. Owen caught only a few broken phrases, thought he was rambling in drink. 'A ghost — ghost risen up from the past — Johnny McEntaggart — God skewer me, the bloody field at Malplaquet — I found him — we went out in the morning to bury the enemy dead — leg smashed at the knee —I saved his life, got him on to a hospital-cart — weren't we from the one townland — Johnny McEntaggart, "stupidissimus Catholicus sempiterne damnatus," fighting as always on the losing side. God skewer me, d'you tell me he is still alive?'

Later, when the old soldier quietened down, he became the schoolmaster. 'What Latin do you know, boy?' Owen stammered he had learned enough Latin from the Priest at Aughrim to answer him at Mass.

'Well, you'll have to forget all that if you want to stay here. You'll go with my scholars every Sunday to hear the Reverend Dr. Goldsmith read the Service in good King's English at Lissoy. You needn't, of course, listen to him, but that's your own look-out. And you'll pay me ten shillings a quarter for the Latin, six for Mathematics, five for Grammar and Composition in English, and an equal sum for French, if that's the direction your uncultivated Connachtman's legs are heading for.'

'I have it here, sir.'

'Oh you have, eh?' He eyed the fistful of coins Owen took eagerly from his pocket. 'And that puts me in mind . . . you'll need a lodging. I've already as many scholars lodging as the room will hold, but now, if I was to set you up a straw mattress in the hen-house . . .'

Early next morning Owen followed the great bulk of the Quartermaster up a sandy by-road between clumps of heather, tall ferns and bare slabs of limestone, while the larks went singing up into the limitless midland sky. There by the roadside, as if it had grown up out of the rock and furze, thatched and limewashed, stood the school. It was full of a roaring sound. Half a hundred boys, from little things of five years old to big six-foot lads were rehearsing — crying out aloud each his own lesson, in three different languages, all together, from dozens of different books, papers and slates. The roar increased when the Quartermaster darkened the door.

His voice cut through the din. 'Reilly!' A tall dark boy of about sixteen came forward. The Quartermaster took his book from him, handed it to Owen. 'This is the History of the Bloody Wars in France, by General Julius Caesar. Teach him, Reilly.'

The pair sat on a pine log under the smoke-browned map of the World. 'I'm Philip Reilly of Kells. Who are you?'

'Owen Kelly of Aughrim.'

Philip looked at him quickly. 'Going for the Church?' he asked. 'Maybe,' said Owen, not knowing how he should answer. 'Well anyhow, this is the way it starts,' said Philip, fingering the words "Omnis Gallia est in tres partes divisa," which is, All Gaul — that's France, not Galway — is in three parts divided. Now read it.' Owen raised his voice to join the wild babel of tongues.

Before they broke at noon for a drink of milk and a bite of bread from their satchels, he had the first two pages of General Julius Caesar off by heart.

A FINE DAY in August, three months later. Owen and Philip Reilly sat on a rock with their bare feet in the stream. They had a fishing rod set to catch trout, and were translating into English the Twentyfirst Part of Livy's History of Republican Rome which they had copied out in ink from the Quartermaster's book. The rest of the scholars had gone to their homes for a few weeks' break, all but themselves and young Goldsmith, the Rector's son, a dull little boy of nine who was in charge of the fishing-rod.

In the quiet, Philip confided to Owen that he was studying for the Priesthood. His uncle in Belgium would pay for him in the Irish College in France. For the first time Owen heard the name — Douai. 'They teach you everything there,' said Philip, 'but you have to know your Latin and Greek to get in.'

'Would it cost much?'

'Oh, a few hundred crowns, I expect.'

Owen thought wistfully of how his own small store of money was dwindling. Maybe he could earn enough — but just then young Goldsmith began to shout and tug at the rod.

WINTER. Short dark days. Owen got up early

in the frost of the mornings to catch the daylight for Caesar and Livy and Gough's Theory of Arithmetick, and save the cost of candles. He had more than £5 put by, earned by leather-work up at the Rectory and among the Goldsmith uncles and cousins who were all fox-hunting men and hard on horse leather and riding-boots. Christmas coming, Philip said he must go. He had learned all the Latin on the Quartermaster's shelves, and now he must start on Greek. Up North, far away among the tangle of lakes in Fermanagh, there was rumoured to be a Master in hiding who taught Catholic boys Homer and the New Testament in Greek. On the spur of the moment Owen said he would go with him.

He thanked Quartermaster Byrne for all he had taught him, gave him a precious History he had brought from Aughrim, and bought him a bottle of whiskey in the tavern at Lissoy. 'God be with ye, gentlemen,' said the Quartermaster. 'O'Reilly one day will be "Sacerdos Magnus," a Soggarth More, as they say; and likely be hanged for it. But God skewer me if the pupil of John McEntaggart will ever wear clerical cloth!'

Six weeks it took them, through rain and sleet and the mud of the laneways. Owen had made half-a-dozen pair of brogues which they carried on their shoulders hung from straps and sold at fairs in the towns they passed. At Manorhamilton, they bought a bundle of paper from a cheapjack stall, and a dozen quills which Owen cut to make pens. They never lingered in towns, but hurried out into the rutted country roads again, and went to ramshackle wayside inns to buy bread and cheese, sparing every copper they could. Sometimes a Williamite farmer — you would know him by his gaiters and watch-chain — would let them sleep the night in a hayloft or a chicken-house, and they would lie close together for warmth, reciting pages of Caesar or lists of Latin verbs to one another until their tired brains slept. More often they sought shelter in the cabins of the poor, where they were let warm their feet at the fire without question. The whole family would gather round the blaze to hear Philip play the tin whistle and to hear Owen tell stories of the ancient Irish Kings and Republican Rome.

So they passed through Longford, the Leitrim Hills, across the wasteland of Cavan, crowded with cottages, up over the shoulder of Slieve Rushen white with snow, until far below them they glimpsed the cold floodwaters of Lough Erne.

Along the lakeside, in a tangle of scrub-oak and alder, they plodded through the poorest places Owen had ever seen. Hovels of rough stone without mortar, the smoke leaking through all the chinks in the stone. And huts of hazel boughs, mud-plastered, thatched with reeds. And people everywhere, women covered in dark shawls from head to foot, men dressed like scare-crows, netting the waterfowl with which the marshes teemed. Their Northern voices were curiously birdlike and cheerful, and they were so friendly that the scholars lost all fear of Informers and boldly asked where could they find the Master of Greek.

'Aye. That'll be Laxy Turnbull ye'll be wanting. It's a long day's journey and a tricksome one, up the River Arney way. Bide ye the night within, and I'll take ye up by water come the day.'

Next day, in a long black canoe, their teeth chattering with the cold, they were out on the waters of Lough Erne.

On Kuldy Island

THE FIRST THING they learned on the island was how to build themselves a hut. They were shown how to do it by the other scholars — there seemed very few of them — who were there already. The hut was made in the manner of a gipsy tent, with boughs of ash and hazel fixed in the ground, bent and tied together on top, then interlaced with branches and twigs. They cut reeds and osiers where they grew in giant ranks by the lakeside, and thatched the little hut right down to the ground with them. Owen and Philip, being tall boys, had not room to stand up inside. They bedded down on bundles of rush and fern, with the Cobbler's old horse-blanket from his Army days to cover them. Later, they had blankets of the skins of otters and hares, which Owen sewed together and stuffed with wildfowl feathers. A similar rug of animal furs closed the little doorway and kept out the biting wind.

Apart from the screaming of waterfowl, Kuldy Island was the quietest place Owen had ever known. The bleak light of the water was reflected from the rocks and the bare branches of the trees, making all the faces look pale and ghostly; and when he went by the lakeside in the dawn to see what fish he might have caught on his nightlines, he often felt he was living in a dream, or as if he had got himself lost in the pages of some ancient history.

Philip had grown pale and thin from the hardships of the road. He spent the first few weeks shivering, wrapped in a blanket, while Owen used his hands and his wits to keep him warm and well fed..

It took him a while to get used to the language of the scholars who lived in huts, half a dozen or so, among the trees or in the shelter of a rock.

They spoke Irish, but their voices were strangely tuneful and birdlike, and their Irish sounded different from the Irish he had heard amongst the old people back home in Aughrim when he was a child. But he was quick at the tongues and soon able to converse with them, and even to answer back the jokes which they loved. They called him 'An Connachtach,' and with his knife and his Latin, his knowledge of Sarsfield stories and his comical Galway songs, he was looked upon as a curiosity.

But what they most valued Owen for, and Philip too, was their English. These boys were Maguires, Gallaghers, O'Husseys, and big raw-boned O'Donnells, all secretly studying for the Colleges in Rome, Salamanca, or the Universities in Belgium and France. Latin would take them through the Universities and the Priestly Colleges, where it was the spoken tongue; but French and English were a rarity, hard to come by in this wilderness of woods and water, and of the utmost value in the Army, Law, Medicine, and in the Trade of the European Towns.

So they would often come to the hut of Philip and Owen, bringing presents of salmon and gulls' eggs, to learn the English names of things, and English weights and money, and to learn to read from Owen's book, 'The Life of Moll Flanders, a Woman of Fortune,' which Owen had got for a couple of rabbit-snares from young Goldsmith, the Rector's son. And the two boys in their turn learned the lovely Irish in which these Northerners could talk of everything under the stars — of the escape of Red Hugh from Dublin Castle in the snow, of the young Bonnie Prince Charlie who was preparing a mighty army in France to return and sweep the English Williamites into the sea, and of the treasures of gold and rich cattle-lands that were said to be had for the taking, beyond the Western Ocean, in Hy Brasil, the Land of the Red Man's Son. Owen wished he could write it all down, but though they could all write Latin, and some of them Greek, not one of them could write a word of his own delightful tongue.

With their strange language, their fierce pride in their families, their strange names — Colm and Conall and Hughdy and Aughy and Art — Owen more than ever felt he had been spirited back into ancient times.

They looked after themselves on the island, fed themselves by fishing and hunting, cooked at the stone hearths they had made outside their huts. Owen, and Philip too when he recovered from his fever, had to be tough to keep up with them. They played a fierce game called Winter Camán, lashing at a horse-hair ball with bent sticks, along a flat reach by the lakeside, and even waist-deep into the icy water. Owen learned to defend himself and to give as good as he got with the crooked sticks.

But the Northmen grew suddenly serious when they returned to their huts and lit rush-lights to study their books. Mingled with the cry of the waterfowl, their voices would rise from the huts, reciting passages of Greek and Latin, the Theorems of Euclid's Geometry, parts and persons of French and English verbs. Breakfast before dawn, then as the first light glimmered they would go, one by one in their turn, hair combed and cleanest neckcloth on, into the house of the Master.

THE FIRST TIME Owen laid eyes on Laxy Turnbull, he was in bed. A rush-candle stood in an earthen dish by the bedside, revealing a short bulk under a knitted quilt from which the feathers were spilling. Slowly a round red face rose up into the light. There was a bald patch like a monk's tonsure on the crown of his head, with a fuzz of snow-white hair all round it. Owen was reminded of the picture of a Saint he had seen in an ancient book. He realised with a start that the sharp Northern voice was speaking to him, in Latin. The only word he recognised was 'Libros' (books). With trembling fingers he took a bundle of his handwritten books from his satchel and handed them to the saintly figure on the bed. Short thick fingers riffled the papers, took a sheet, thrust it at him, crying, 'Lege!' (read).

It was Livy's story of the Siege of Syracuse. Owen read it out in his best Quartermaster Byrne Latin accent. The big head with the monkish halo lay to one side, with eyes closed and ear cocked to hear the exact sound of every syllable. Owen lost himself in the words and the wonderful rhythms that gave the very feeling of being in the middle of the fierce Battle for the Town — until he was cut short by the command, 'Construe!' which he knew meant, 'translate'. He began to tell the story word for word in English, using the tone he had learned from listening to Dr. Goldsmith in the Protestant Church. The red face, smooth and shining as a baby's, was suddenly pushed close to him, and dim blue eyes peered at him closely.

'I see,' said the sharp voice, mimicking his Goldsmith tones, 'we have a cultivated young Barbarian. What brings your Lordship here?'

'I want the Greek, sir.'

'You will kindly address me as Doctor.'

'Yessir . . . Doctor.'

The Doctor sat upright — Owen now saw that he had two or three coats on under the bedclothes — and took a slim yellow book from the shelf at the back of the bed. 'Your Lordship will copy out from this the Greek Alphabet, the sample words, sentences, and translations into Latin. You have until sunset to learn the first ten lessons.'

'"Gratias," Doctor. How much will it be?'

Doctor Turnbull's rosy face grew rosier. 'My dear young Barbarian,' he said in toothless bitter English, 'you are not buying a bullock at a Galway fair. Your money will not buy the language of Socrates or St. John. You will pay me by learning what I teach!'

He laid his white halo back on the pillow and seemed to sleep. With fluttering heart, Owen tiptoed out of the house.

DURING THE COLD WEATHER the Doctor remained in bed to keep himself warm. The scholars took it in turn to tidy his room, fill his leather bucket with spring water, cook for him and bring him his breakfast — a kind of porridge made of pulped potatoes and beans, with water-cress when it was in season and a mug of goat's milk. Propped up in bed with the wooden platter of food before him, he would read and eat for an hour, and then ring the small brass bell. One by one, beginning with Peregrine O'Donnell, the Chief Scholar, and down to little Farfassa O'Hussey who was only starting on the Tables of Number and Latin nouns, they would come to recite their task and be taught the next one.

They were in awe of his immense learning, his mastery of all the damp old leathery books that lay piled anyway on the ramshackle shelves. They feared his anger, his face reddening, his cutting tongue. If a task were neglected or badly done he would say, 'Have the goodness, young man, to hand me the Speaker.' This was a stout leather strap which hung from a peg, and it was so called because, as the Doctor said, 'it speaks the only language that lazy bones can understand.'

Sometimes a smile softened his eyes, like winter sunlight on a frozen pond, and he would say, 'Bene, puer,' at a task well done. At such times they loved him, and felt they were getting somewhere on the vast seas of learning that lay between them and the Universities of the world.

Among themselves they called him 'Laxy.' And as 'Laxy Turnbull' his fame was known to all the mainland for miles about. They gossiped of him, told what they had heard. That he was born in the East, in Belfast, son of a Catholic linen-merchant. They told how he had walked through the great cities of Europe, playing the fiddle in the streets, and arguing the heads off learned College Professors, in return for a night's lodging. He returned to find his father ruined after King William's victory, and he himself had to go into hiding, hunted by the Law as a Popish schoolmaster.

His house was in the most sheltered part of little Kuldy Island. It was no more than a 'bothán' of loose stones, windowless, thatched with reeds, built up against the thick stone gable of an old ruin buried in ivy and elder-bushes. In the loneliness of the night the scholars would often hear the strains of the violin coming from the house, or his voice raised chanting Greek choruses or intoning the Passion according to St. John.

The Doctor's usual drink was spring water and milk, but from time to time a terrible craving used to come upon him for what the mainland folk called 'the yellow drop.' Then the scholars went in fear and trembling, as the word went round that Laxy was suffering from 'an Triomach Mór,' the Great Thirst. At such a time the very sound of the brass bell in the morning, harsh and jangling and an hour too early, said clearly, 'an Triomach Mór.'

There was a causeway across to the mainland, built in times long gone by. A couple of the senior scholars would slip by night across the causeway and seek in the cabins of the fishermen and fowlers for a drop of mountain whiskey or home-made beer. The boy looking after the house would slip it quietly among the Doctor's books. Then everything would brighten up, and once again the strains of Scots jigs and Spanish dances played on the violin would be heard after dark and the deep rich voice intoning the Greek.

FROM THE FIRST MORNING that Philip Reilly and himself lay on their elbows above the dark old pages, Owen fell in love with Greek. There was a kind of a spoken clarity in the words. He felt that some living voice, long buried in the past, was speaking to him from the page. Philip had taught him Latin; it was his turn now to teach Philip. He was surprised to find that when he shut his eyes a picture of the page remained in his mind, and he could read the words on it just as if the page were in front of him.

Before he was a week in the place he surprised the Doctor by reciting the whole of the story of Arion the Singer, robbed and thrown in the sea by the sailors, and saved by a dolphin who had been lured by his song. When Owen had done he found the dim blue eyes fixed on him.

'What is your father, boy?'

'A shepherd, Doctor, on the lands of the Archdeacon.'

'You have relatives abroad, a priest perhaps, a merchant, an Army captain, who can pay for your University education or perhaps get you a pension from the Catholic Princes?'

'No, Doctor.'

'Ah dear, it's a sad world. Here, child, is another story to learn, written by a Master of Words called Luke. Listen.'

He read the Greek with a musical rise and fall of the voice, and it was clear he was in love with every syllable of it. 'Now it happened that there were certain shepherds minding their flocks by night . . .'

WHEN THE DAYS grew brighter and branches broke in bud, the Doctor got up during the day, and dressed in a long garment with about a hundred buttons. He even ventured out, and stood for awhile on the shore at the open side of the island, gazing out across the waste of water to the faint blue hills. One night he surprised them all out of their huts by ringing the bell after dark.

It was a starlit night. He pointed out the stars and the planets, taught them their names and how they moved. 'Look, gentlemen, those are the Seven Sisters — the plodding Saxon calls them the Plough. The Sisters circle the heavens but, as they do so, those two of them point forever towards the North Pole Star — look — the one fixed star of all. It guides us on our voyages of discovery. Now tell me, who discovered the New World?'

'Columbus,' said Peregrine O'Donnell.

'Brendan the Irishman,' said Owen.

'Neither,' said the Doctor. 'Those men discovered Red Man's Land, just such another world of wine, women and winter as is our own. But the real New World is yet to be discovered. We have been given the map of it, in the Gospels. And the way to it lies through the one word — give.'

PAPER WAS VERY SCARCE. The bundle of it which Owen and Philip had brought was long since written on and made into books, both by themselves and by the Northern boys. No one on the island had any money except Owen. He got permission to go for supplies, along with Peregrine O'Donnell, on the canoes going with hides and fish to the town of Enniskillen, two days' journey up the lake.

The two lads sat in the stern while hardy brown men pulled on three sets of oars. They watched the forests of the mainland go by, and the blue hills crowding along the skyline to the North and West — the hills of Tírchonaill, Peregreine told him, saying his home lay beyond them, down by a creek of the Western Sea. Some day soon now a smuggling ship would come into the creek, bringing the passage-money from his brother in Spain, and he would be off. To Salamanca. Gazing at the far-off peaks, Owen felt a stab of envy.

It was a fair-day in Enniskillen. They felt safe in the crowds of men and beasts. They avoided the shops, bought reams of paper of all sizes, and leather jars of real ink, from the cheapjacks. Poking among the piles of old clothes and harness leathers, Owen discovered a tattered old book in a strange language, the cover gone. Peregrine thought it might be Hebrew. 'Arrah, it's old gibberish Irish,' said the cheapjack and threw it to them for tuppence.

The boatmen brought them into a dark tavern in a narow lane, where they had a meal of tripe and onions and a draught of ale. Owen spent fifteen shillings on two bottles of smuggler's brandy, and hid them in his sack with the books and things. 'We'll keep this hidden,' he said 'until the next "Triomach Mór" '. He reckoned he had about three pounds left in his little hoard.

They were on the water again next morning as the sunrise was streaking the waves with red. He read aloud for Peregrine, who helped to turn it into Irish for the boatmen as they went along.

NEXT TIME HE stood before the Doctor for a lesson, he handed him the tattered Irish book, for which he had made and tooled a fine cover of otterskin. Laxy studied it with interest, and pronounced it to be a translation of the New Testament 'made,' he said, 'for the use of the wild Irish at the command of that curious and very learned woman, Elizabeth of England, Queen.'

He bade Owen pull out a wooden chest from under the bed. It was stuffed full of books. He unwrapped one which was carefully tied up in a piece of sail-cloth, and said, 'Here is a curious thing.' The leaves were of goatskin, tinted a pale violet but yellow with age at the edges and holed by bookworms. The letters were thick and black, but the capital letter beginning each section was almost as large as the page, brightly coloured and twined with strange birds and flowers and animal heads.

'Can you read it?'

'I think it's Latin.'

'It is. It is a Psalter, that is, a copy in Latin of King David's Poems. But look in the margin — what's that?'

Owen puzzled over a scrap of small sharp writing in black ink. Only one word made sense — 'Lon'.

'That might be Irish, Doctor — the word for a blackbird.'

'It is. This is a scrap of Irish verse, written on the edge of this page over a thousand years ago, by the scribe in some Great School when he got tired copying the Latin text.

'Blackbird among the buds
you sing sweet and no wonder
since you haven't to wear your feathers out
like me, copying long words.'

'A thousand years!' breathed Owen. Again, he had the feeling given him by the Greek, that a voice had suddenly spoken to him from the silent page.

'I got that book from an old man dying on the shores of Belfast Lough. For generations before him his fathers had been Keepers of the Book.'

Birthday of a Master

TWO YEARS had passed. Owen, touching 17, was now a young man, tall, his beard beginning, his dark honeycoloured hair hanging in curling hanks tied behind with a leather thong. There wasn't a spare inch of flesh on his body; he was as hardy as nails from the open-air life, the wrestling, the Winter 'Camán', climbing, carrying timber and coursing the mainland hares with the boys on their Fridays off.

Philip, at 18, dark, with a bit of black beard trimmed to a sharp point, was now the most advanced of Laxy's students, and was wondering how to get in touch with his uncle in Belgium.

Ever since the day he had brought the tuppenny Irish book to him as a present from Enniskillen, Laxy never used the Speaker on Owen — though his eyes had often flickered in that direction. Instead, he piled on him the hardest tasks, making him read Plato's 'Republic' in Greek, learn hundreds of lines of Ovid's Latin Stories in verse of the Adventures of the Pagan Gods and Girls turned into Trees and Beasts. And then he asked him to do — what he never asked even Philip — to write these stories in Irish and English verse, and even make little songs of them in French to tunes which he played for Owen on his violin.

To crown it all, he gave him three Compositions to write every Saturday (the other boys only got two), one in Greek, one in Latin, and one in French, English or Irish, which he called the 'vulgar tongues'.

The Doctor never seemed to be pleased. He covered Owen's Poems and Compositions all over with angry red corrections, and only once in a blue moon wrote 'Bene' at the bottom. Once, during the usual Friday concert at his house, he read the boys a story in Latin from a manuscript book. It was called, 'A Journey on Foot from Rome to Muscovy,' and he offered the prize of a red apple to the boy who could tell him which of the famous authors of old had written it.

Philip grinned suddenly and said, 'An Connachtach!'

'How did you know?' asked the Doctor, giving him the apple.

'I recognised the picture of the traveller playing the tin whistle for a night's lodging at the poor man's fire in the forests of Austria.'

'But there are no poor peasants in Austria,' Hughdy Gallagher objected. 'It is a Catholic country.'

'The poor are the poor everywhere,' said the Doctor. 'Never forget them. Remember your Greek — "Whatsoever you do unto these my unfortunate ones, you do it to Me!" '

He ordered Hughdy to put more logs on the fire until it blazed up in light and warmth against the winter night outside. And taking his violin he played and taught them a little French dancing-song to which Owen had set words in Irish:

> 'Inniu, lá is gile den tseacht,
> Inniu, ní gá caoineadh,
> Inniu, tá an lá linn,
> Gintear i gCríost sinn, Dé hAoine!'

THE CLOTHES they had brought with them were long since worn into rags. Owen had made breeches of otterskin for Philip and himself, and had stitched together wonderful fur jackets of rabbitskins, and cocky-looking caps to match with flaps that fastened under their manly beards. With rawhide pampooties on their feet, and fur mittens, they stalked about the island like young lords. The rest of the boys wouldn't be dead or alive till they got fur jackets and fancy caps like that, so that Owen was kept busy with his knife and needle.

DURING THESE YEARS they grew to talk and think like the Doctor. They learned to view the living world of the past, and the unseen world of the present that lay beyond the lakes and woodlands, through his eyes. And Laxy — with his fuzz of white hair, his strange cries in the night, his startling ideas about everything, his growing fits of drowsiness in the middle of a lesson, his sudden shafts of insight into their most secret selves — was a constant surprise to them.

Every Friday was his Birthday. No lessons that day. They could sleep for an hour or two longer than usual, and enjoy a long and cheerful breakfast. The bell would ring about noon, and they would all assemble at the Master's house, where even though the snow lay thick on the thatch they would find him up, dressed in his long robe, with white neckcloth, and boots which

Owen had mended and polished with goose-grease mixed with cobbler's ink until they shone.

They sat where they could, on the bed, on the floor strewn with fresh rushes. Laxy sat in a súgán chair by the hearth, and read aloud to them in Greek from a big book with his eyes closed. Always the same story. The Passion of Christ according to St. John.

Then he would talk to them in homely tones, in Irish. And tell them why the day of the Death of Christ was no time for fasting and moaning, but a feastday, the birthday into the New Life, the New Insight, the New World of ever wandering and never satisfied Man.

Free for the rest of the afternoon, they went leaping and laughing along the causeway, climbing trees on the mainland, gathering nuts and berries and wild apples in season, hunting hares with their dogs, riding bare-back on the half-wild horses that grazed the shores of the Lake, or fishing with the 'Fir Manach' in their black canoes. Home then at dusk, ravenous, to grill salmon outside their huts, or to bake wildfowl in an oven of hot stones covered over with earth. When the oven was opened their teeth would water at the delicious smell that rose from the roast duck.

Afterwards, a concert of music and songs in many tongues at the Master's house. Until at last the Master put aside his violin and reminded them of their Saturday tasks, and the birthday was over for another week.

ANOTHER WINTER was at hand and already they were shaping bent sticks for the 'Camán'. One Friday evening after the firelit feast, when they assembled at the Master's house they found him stretched on the bed, fully robed, the pewter mug fallen by the bedside, the brandy spilled. His blue Northern eyes were frozen in death. Philip joined his hands before they stiffened, and closed his eyes. Owen found his hands trembling, his voice stuck in his throat.

There was no Priest. A couple of old women came from the mainland, lit candles and keened. Then the mainland people, men, women and children thronged across the causeway. Those who could not find place in the little house lit a big bonfire outside, and made merry for three nights with music and mummeries and the yellow drop.

Owen took the axe and in a kind of desperate rage chopped out planks of ash and alder to make a rude coffin. They buried him in the shelter of the ancient gable-end where he used to sit on sunny days teaching them Wisdom. Philip read aloud in Greek, the Passion from the Gospel of John. Owen set a board on the wall at the grave's head. He had carved the inscription with his leather-knife:

Here
Our Dear Master
Alexander Turnbull
Doctor of the Sacred Books
Entered the New World
Nov. 3 A.D. 1740

The Hidden Treasure

BLACK WERE THE WINTER DAYS, the nights were empty. Hughdy Gallagher disappeared. Philip took charge. But he had neither the voice nor the authority of the Doctor; the scholars grew idle, impudent, failed to answer when he rang the bell, and as often as not spent their nights in the huts of the mainland, story-telling, and dancing with the girls.

A change come over Owen under the shock of the death. He neglected his books, neglected his food, neglected his hair and his clothes. He would spend hours staring dumbly at the Master's house. Or staring along the causeway, half expecting to see a new Master coming out of the woods. But no one came; there was only the grey rain on the meaningless waste waters of the lake.

The nights were unbearable, haunted by the Doctor's voice. He could not bear to open a book, for every syllable reminded him of that sharp Northern voice which he realised now he had loved. He took to going at night to a ramshackle tavern at a mainland cross-roads, spending his money on drink with the wilder boys, and coming home before dawn to the lonely island, a crowd of them singing aloud drunkenly arm-in-arm.

One morning Philip shook him out of a stupid sleep. 'Get up, "a Chonnachtaigh". We're getting out of here!'

He obeyed like a child. They packed their few things. They entered the Master's house for a last look round, and to take some keepsake of their dead teacher. Philip took the little violin. Owen rummaging blindly among the books, came upon the poor old goatskin book wrapped in sailcloth, in which Laxy had shown him his first Irish poem. He shut his eyes tight, gripped his fists, as wave after wave of sheer agony flowed over his body. 'Master, Master,' he said bitterly through his teeth, 'why have you done this to us?' He pushed the poor relic into his pack, and staggered out.

TWO NIGHTS LATER they were in Enniskillen. They turned North. A long tramp of wet weeks brought them to the salt water. Lough Swilly.

At a sailor's inn they played dice with a thick-set man in a knitted red cap, the locks of his hair glued together with tar. He was the Captain of a Dutch fishing smack, and spoke in a mixture of broken Irish and terrible French. 'Shah', he would smuggle them to the Belgian coast, 'shah, certanymong', for five English pounds apiece.

Owen had six pounds thirteen shillings. He offered the money to Philip. Philip refused. During the night, he rose, slipped the six pounds into Philip's pocket, kept the odd shillings for himself, and disappeared into the night.

THE MONTHS that followed were among the weariest he had ever known. Often in later life he had nightmares of that time. He had to start all over again. Plodding from village to village, town to town, buying scraps of leather and bits of wool, doing odd jobs of mending at the tidy farmhouses of the Williamite folk, selling his little stock of brogues at the fairs, putting penny to penny to make a shilling, putting shilling to shilling till he had a gold sovereign to sew in the tail of his coat; in sickness often, he was in terrible dejection most of the time, often with nothing to eat but a turnip stolen from a planter's field, and the odd sup of milk begged from a dairymaid. He fell in with a troupe of Gipsies, travelled with them in their bright wagons a whole Summer, learned their lingo, did all their leatherwork, made fancy articles which the Gipsy women and children sold by the dozen from door to door, and shared the money. And at last, when Kuldy Island had faded to a dim memory, he opened his books again.

Around the camp-fire the Gipsies were surprised to find that the fierce and serious young Cobbler could play the fiddle and make fantastic songs. Their leader, Cabalengro, a small brown man with big gold rings in his ears, finding that the Cobbler could write down the songs too, took the sheets into a printing-house in Dundalk town. The gipsies sang them and sold them at fairs, wakes, weddings and taverns, and made a hatful of money, which they shared.

From them Owen learned the horse business. And one mild August evening he found himself with Cabalengro walking aboard a ship at Drogheda, no questions asked by the Law Agents on the Quay, no penny to pay, in charge of a herd of horses bound for the Pas de Calais in the North of France.

He breathed deeply of the salt air as if it was freedom. The bows riding the green wave fascinated him, the wind made harp-music in the ropes of the rigging, the Hills of Ireland disappeared in the Autumn haze.

'Farewell,' he wrote, 'Island of poverty,
I am well quit of your wind and your wave
And the fogs of your comical kind stupidity
That let my Master die and danced on his
grave.'

CALAIS. A firm handgrip, a flash of white teeth, and Cabalengro was gone. Owen walked in a daze along the sunlit pavement, stared in delight at the flash of glass, the pretty Catholic girls with long laced boots twinkling under clean petticoats, the tall stone Catholic spires.

At last the high road led him by a gate in the ancient fortifications into the City of Douai. Magic name. He had heard it long ago, from Philip, at Lissoy.

He couldn't stop, but hurried along under the house-fronts overhanging the pavements, past the heavy horse-drawn drays, past the tall dark chimneys of the breweries and the gun factories, till he came to the high walls of the University.

It took his breath away. He had thought it might be something like Kuldy Island, only larger. It was very much larger indeed. It was a City in itself. Paved streets, alleyways, gardens and orchards, Colleges everywhere, a forest of turrets and spires. Monks, Priests, Doctors in red robes, Scholars in long gowns with hoods, and Scholars in their shirt sleeves playing at tennis. He inquired the way to 'Le Collège des Irlandais'

Inside the gate of the Irish College, with beating heart, he asked for Master Philip O'Reilly of Kells. The porter went down the names in his roll of students with a swarthy thumb. There was no such student. The day darkened around Owen. He was utterly alone, and had but ten English pounds in French money to his name.

The porter, looking dubiously at his ragged beard, his Gipsy clothes, his bulging pack, shrugged and said in thick French that the Examination for Entrants would be held the first week in September. 'But it is, of course, for the sons of gentlemen. Not for the poor, like you and me, comrade,' he added, shutting the book.

OWEN SAT the Examination with five other young Irishmen, well dressed, sure of themselves. It went on for a week. Greek Grammar, Latin Grammar, Greek Literature, Latin Literature, the Christian Gospels, Ancient History, the Science of Wisdom, the Science of Argument, Arithmetic, Algebra, the Theorems of Euclid, the Knowledge of Stars . . . All answers to be in Latin. Closing his eyes he saw the pages of the old handwritten books in his mind, heard the voice of Laxy in his ears, wrote, wrote, wrote.

They were fed and lodged at the Guest House. On the Sunday morning after Mass, they went to the door of the Examination Hall where the results were posted up. Incredibly, he saw his name — 'Eugenius O'Kelly Aughrimensis' — at the top of the list. And, incredibly, after his name he saw the word which meant 'Excluded'.

A red rage got him as far as the Rector's room. A thin face with spiky upturned moustachios and goatee beard, informed him that the University was an expensive place, that he was not supported by a parent or relation, that he had no pension from a Priestly Order or from the King. Owen said he was a tradesman, and could work in the town at his trade until he had enough money to pay the fees. The Rector, swinging a thin gold chain from which a cross hung about his neck, shrugged, said trades in France were regulated by the Unions, that he would have to serve his time to a master-shoemaker before he would be allowed to earn for himself.

'How long, Father Rector?'

'From five to seven years.'

Outside again, deafened by Sunday bells, he felt like tearing the whole town up by the roots. 'How right Laxy was — the poor are the poor everywhere!' he muttered. He entered a tavern, decided to get savagely drunk.

He had filled his brandy-glass for the third

time when a hand was laid on his shoulder. 'O'Kelly of Aughrim? Father Luke wants to speak with you.'

'Who's Father Luke?' he glowered.

'Our Librarian.'

For the first time in his life, Owen stood in a Library. Tall lance-windows lighted the stacks of leather-bound volumes, their coloured tassels and title-tags hanging from them, in bays and walls and caverns of shelves. An old greybeard sat at a table. The Rector sat beside him. 'Is this yours, boy?' asked the Greybeard, indicating Owen's old sack of books. He had forgotten it, left it behind in his rage. 'And is this yours too?' He held up the old goatskin book wrapped in sailcloth. Owen nodded.

'You know what it is?'

'Yes, Father. The Poems of David. Copied in Ireland. It is very old.'

Father Luke opened it, smiled, fingered the old, coloured wormholed sheets as if he loved them.

'O'Kelly,' said the Rector in his elegant voice, 'this little book you have brought is one of the most valuable things in the room. If you agree to leave it here with us, it will pay for your lodgings and lectures at the College until you have gained your Master's Degree or your Doctorate, if you work hard enough.'

Owen sat suddenly, covering his eyes as the scalding tears ran down his cheeks.

'Now, what on earth are you weeping for?'

He sobbed. 'For my dead Master.'

To the New World

EASTER DAY, 1745. All the bells in Douai were ringing. The Burghers, the Merchants, the Unions of Craftsmen, with their wives in rich silks and furs, were thronging the Churches to celebrate the great feast of the Christian Year. But in the streets and along the waterways there was no holiday. All day the great drays and the barges passed, laden with cannon, ammunition, tents, field-kitchens, horses, wheat and hay.

It was war. The Armies of Catholic Austria, alongside the Protestant Dutch and English, were swarming into the Lowlands above Douai, to attack the borders of his Most Catholic Majesty Louis XV, King of France. The King himself under his Royal Standard was hastening to the battlefront. Cavalry and infantry, drums beating and banners flying, passed, clattering over the cobbled streets. Among them rode the Earl of Clare; behind him came his mounted troops in their dark green jackets — 'Les Royal Irlandais'.

In the great hall of the University, Owen Kelly stood to take his Master's Degree. All around on the dais in a blaze of coloured robes sat the Professors and Doctors of the Arts, Medicine, Wisdom, and Divinity, while the hall was thronged with the great body of students applauding.

Slim and tall in his blue gown with white hood, his hair and beard curled and perfumed, the young man stood with bowed head, his proud eyes closed respectfully, while the Clerk read out the long list of his victories — The King's Prize in Mathematics, the University Award in Greek, the Pope's Gold Medal in the Science of Wisdom. There was a roar from the students, and even the grave Doctors gently clapped.

That night he gave a feast for his friends, with wine, music, and roast beef. Next morning he was in the Rector's room. The Rector was writing for him a letter of introduction to the Earl of Clare. Cool grey eyes above the spiked moustachios looked at him oddly.

'Young man,' he asked, 'have you never thought of entering the Church?'

'Father,' said Owen, 'I am already "in" the Church.'

The thin lips smiled. 'Oh, you humorous Irish wits — I meant the Priesthood?'

'I am not called,' said Owen.

'I think, somehow, you will be,' murmured the Rector, as he fixed his seal to the letter.

HE LAID OUT the half of his prize-money in buying a Flemish mare with a wicked eye, black riding-boots with silver spurs, breeches of white doeskin, cocked hat with plume, and an immense cloak tied with a gold chain and lined with fur. Then he galloped in style out of the town gates on the highway to the North.

At the water-mills, at the village washing-pools, in the upland fields of turnips and springing corn, poor folk with wooden shoes toiled and carried burdens on their backs. They got out of his way if he met them on the road; the women bowed, the men touched their caps, as he had seen his father do long years ago to the Archdeacon. Behind his back, they spat, growled, 'Another young "aristo". Another game-cock off to these endless highclass wars, that bring nothing only more King's taxes on the bit of bread we put in our mouth. And ruin to our fields.'

The Earl of Clare had his Head-quarters in a farmhouse near the river Schelde, where his Brigade formed part of the French Army surrounding and starving out the town of Tournai. A young 'aide' in a dazzling uniform took the Rector's letter between the tips of two fingers as if it might dirty them, and left Owen standing in the yard. He sauntered back in about an hour's time and beckoned lazily. A long love-curl hung down at one side almost to his waist. Owen followed.

Lord Clare, a heavy man, dark, with patches of weariness under his eyes, sat at a table covered with maps, telescopes, mathematical instruments. 'An O'Kelly and a scholar,' he said in English. 'Can you read?'

'I think so, m'Lord.'

'Horsed?'

'Yes, m'Lord.'

'Good. Take this note to the Quartermaster. He will issue you with uniform, arms, field equipment — don't play cards in the Canteen until you have paid for them. You will join my Staff, among the "aides" — though I suppose like the rest of my young University peacocks you can't add two and two!'

There were about a dozen of them, all very elegant. The 'aide' with the love-curl was O'Hennessy of Cork. That night Owen lost the rest of his prize-money playing cards with them in the Officers' Mess-tent of 'Les Royal Irlandais'.

FIRST WEEK IN MAY, King Louis with his entire Army was racing south. The English, Dutch and the Whitecoat Austrians were pouring through the Lowland water-meadows, to fall on the flank of the French. Owen, remembering the old names — Malplaquet, Oudenarde — was tense with excitement as he galloped across these same Flanders fields which the Cobbler had told him of in the days gone by. He imagined himself charging with drawn sabre upon the ancient enemy.

But it wasn't a bit like that.

As dawn broke on the morning of the 11th, the Earl sat at a table outside his tent, on a low ridge of pasture-land. At both ends of that rising ground — at Antoing on the right, and away to the left at the village of Fontenoy — all hell broke loose. Thunder of cannonade, drums, bugles, shattering volleys of musket-fire. But nothing to be seen, except 'aides' bent low in the saddle galloping with messages, and thick clouds of smoke drifting on the morning air.

On the table were maps, field glasses, pens and ink, a large Dutch time-piece, a bottle of wine and a leg of mutton, cold.

Owen wrote at speed to the Earl's barked dictation, filed the messages, marked on each the time it was handed in, made sketch-maps and little drawings which he pinned to the orders — 'Red Barn' — 'Peas Field' 'Bushy-top Trees' — 'O'Connors Third, right, Red Barn to Square Tower' — 'Peas Field forward to Red Barn' — 'Crooked Cross back in reserve to Bushy-top Trees.' It was like playing at draughts. As the Earl read the maps and the messages, close-packed troops of mounted men were moved like pieces in a game, more than half a mile away from the din of the two battles.

At one o'clock in the sweltering afternoon, the Earl asked Owen to order lunch. Owen stretched his weary limbs. A messenger bearing the pennant of Marshal Saxe came galloping wildly up from Fontenoy. The Earl snapped the message, read, rose suddenly to his full height, demanded, 'How many?'

'Fourteen thousand, my Lord. English. Under the Duke of Cumberland.'

In a second the Earl had his plumed hat on, was in the saddle, ordering his bugler to sound the 'Charge!' O'Hennessy going before him on a black stallion bore the banner of the Brigade – the blue Flag of Ireland with Silver Harp. Along the ridge, bugle after bugle sang out the 'Charge!'

Owen on his wicked mare was caught up in the wild rush. Over the ridge. There below them they lay, the Redcoats, a scarlet stream pouring between the wood and the ridge, massed thick as far as the eye could see. Wild cries rose above the thundering hooves. 'Remember Limerick!' 'Athlone!' 'Derry and the Boyne!' 'Remember Aughrim!'

The mare sailed over a basket fence. In the air, Owen suddenly felt as if he had been kicked by a mule in the shoulder. Next minute he was sprawled on the earth, while the dense charge thudded over him.

HE LIVED. Coming up to Christmas, a thin skeleton of a man, shivering in the cold of Paris, came into the courtyard of the Earl of Clare. The bullet had been extracted, his broken bones had been repaired, but he would never ride a horse again. Lord Clare succeeded in getting him a couple of months' back-pay, and a decoration from the King for his part in the resounding victory of Fontenoy. He looked for O'Hennessy, to pay him what he owed at cards, but the boy with the love-curl was among the 15,000 dead.

Time hung on his hands. He slept a good deal, ate well, slowly regained his strength. Walking in the streets of Paris, he saw the poor at close quarters. Men swept snow and slush from the streets, their feet bound with rags. Others carried heavy bundles of logs on their backs to sell at the back-doors of the rich. Little children, wrapped in old clothes and blankets, hard to tell whether they were boys or girls, went to work almost as soon as they could walk.

All his great learning seemed to belong to a different world, far removed from life.

Spring coming, he felt restless. He could return to the University, work for his Doctorate, become a Professor. Or he could enter the Civil

Service of the King. In either case, he saw nothing but dull, easy, well-paid life stretching before him: a poor thing after the excitement of Fontenoy.

In his dreams at night he was haunted by faceless multitudes, and a wild cry ringing in his ears, 'Remember Aughrim!'

He wandered up among the great seaport cities of the Belgian coast. He might go into trade. He had some vague idea of seeking out Philip O'Reilly's uncle who, he believed, was in the shipping business. One evening at Ostend, he gazed at the masts of vessels crowding the harbour, thick as trees, bearing cargoes from Africa, the Far East, the lands and islands of the New World. There was excitement in the salt tang of the wind blowing in from the black North Sea. He would sail to the New World!

Passing a bookstall, his eyes fell on a tall volume. 'The World in Pictures, A Book for Children, by Johann Komenius. Done into the Vulgar Tongue and printed at Brussels, 1700.' He bought it, went into a tavern, ordered a glass of red wine, opened a page at random. Surprised, he saw that the whole page, almost, was taken up with a bright, coloured picture of a red man wearing feathers in his hair. Below, there were only three lines of print, very large, very clear:

'Big Eagle is a Red Man.
He lives in a wig-wam.
A wig-wam is a house made of skins.'

Picture after picture, page after page, he turned. 'Hans is a sea-man. He sails in a ship.' — 'This is a moun-tain in Swit-zer-land.' — 'There are no snakes in Ire-land.' He smiled. Drowsed with the red wine, and with the memory of his own childish voice, reading, reading . . . he slept.

In a dream, he seemed to be among flowering hawthorn trees. Two small figures, hair tangled in their eyes, held up dirty fingers, each holding a silver shilling. The shillings turned to golden sovereigns as he looked.

He awoke. The tavern had grown dark. He felt an immense sense of ease within him. Clutching the book, he tipped the serving-girl a whole crown and went out into the cold wind, laughing. 'The New World!' he said. 'Ha-ha! Red Man's Land! Dear God, what an adventure!'

Two days later, he was on board the 'Prinz Wilhelm', laden with tobacco and tin baths, and bound for the Port of Waterford.

The Fire at Wolfhill

THE PRIEST IS OLD. His white hair waves in the wind. Slow clouds are piled above in the limitless midland skies. All the townland of Wolfhill, mostly barefoot, in their frieze jackets, in their dark shawls, are gathered in Dominic Maloney's shearing-pens, between the loft and the tidy house, to hear Mass.

The Priest leaves the Table, climbs a few steps of the stone stairs to the hayloft, turns to face them. He has an announcement to make. He reads the notice from a foolscap sheet, written in a beautiful hand:

'Mr. Owen Kelly, Master of Arts, humbly begs leave to announce that he has arrived in Wolfhill.'

There is a stir among the shawls, the bawneens, the grey frieze coats. They sense the drama of the moment. This is a challenge to the Law.

'Kelly begs leave to say that he is qualified to teach Reading, Spelling, Writing, Arithmetic, and Book-Keeping according to the Italian method.'

There were murmurs from the crowd: 'Praise be to God!' 'Look at that now!'

'To those who wish to pursue the higher studies, Kelly begs leave to announce that he is skilled in the Latin and Greek tongues, and fully qualified to teach History, the Geography of the Globe, Algebra and the Elements of Euclid, Surveying, Mensuration, Astronomy, Navigation, Poetry, Music, and the Irish Tongue.'

'A bhuí le Dia!' cried an old woman, spreading her hands to the sky. She was near a hundred years of age, and was called Nellie the Juck.

'Kelly, in conclusion, begs leave to announce that he will talk to parents this evening, in Dominic Maloney's house, after dark.' Their sidelong glances stray to where Maloney kneels. A strong farmer, he owns five acres — all that is left him of the Maloney pasture-lands.

The Priest moving his sharp glance from face to face, tells them that this is the mercy of God to Wolfhill. He asks them to do all honour to the Teacher who has come so unexpectedly among them. He asks them to build him a bit of a shelter in some lonesome corner against the wet days. To send him one or more boys from every household, no matter at what cost to themselves. And to see that the business is kept from certain ears.

THAT NIGHT by the turf-fire in Maloney's kitchen, they meet the man himself. They are surprised to find him none other than the travelling shoemaker who has parked his little donkey-van by the ruin on the Gracefield Road. He looks like a man young in years, old in the bitter experience of a bitter world. A tall fellow, hollow-cheeked, with an ironic eye and a grin tucked into the corner of his mouth. His homespun breeches are threadbare at the knees, but his neckcloth is clean, his boots well kept.

'How much, Master, for one gossoon to learn the beginnin's?'

'Spelling, one shilling a quarter, Reading, one and ninepence, Writing, two shillings. Arithmetic, three shillings and sixpence.'

'Oh, glory be to God, it's a ferocious price!'

'Get on with you, Patcheen Cray,' cries a neighbour. 'Sure we all know you want to get your son able to write his name, and get a job with a hard hat with the Navigation Company, like Leary's Tomasheen that came home from Sallymanca!'

'Maybe now, Master, you might take a bageen o' pitaties in part payment?'

'Maybe I might!' The ironic grin bites deeper in his cheeks. Before the month is out he knows he will have more 'pitaties' to his name than would feed the townland.

NEXT EVENING, when the sunset is smouldering in the West, the men of the townland come from their day's labour in the cornfields and milking-sheds, the coal pits, quarries and brick-works, bringing their spades and their mattocks, to build the school.

They choose a dry spot among the flat limestone rocks, far from the main roads, a place of goat-paths and rabbit-tracks and fern-fringed pools where the wild duck come in the Winter. It is screened from the inquisitive eye by a wilderness of hazel and furze. They clear a flat area, about 14 feet long and 10 feet wide, in the shelter of a rocky scarp. Dominic Maloney marks out the site and makes the measurements. Before dark the walls have risen to their full height — the front wall five feet high, the back wall by the rock a couple of feet higher to give a slope to the roof. They leave a gap for the doorway. There is no window; in dark days the scholars will have all the light they want in the blaze of the fire of turf and furze.

Another evening sees the roof put on, bog-scraws laid over deal branches. They leave a sizeable hole in the middle of the roof to let the smoke out.

Meanwhile, red clay is brought from the mud-pits in donkey-baskets. They shovel it in and beat it flat with the backs of spades to make the floor.

Connor na gCluck, a sorrowful string of a man with a drooping grey moustache, a head-stone-maker from Timahoe, is driven over by the Priest himself in his pony-cart, bringing the new hearthstone and the tools of his trade. It is unloaded at the side of the high road, and carried the half-mile by tracks through the fern and furze to the schoolhouse door. All the men remove their caps. It is a fine piece of pale granite — only God and Connor know where it came from — the date is cut into the stone: A.D. 1746.

SATURDAY NIGHT and a May moon. The townland of Wolfhill is emptied, young and old are gone to the schoolhouse, packed inside and out. The Priest blesses the hearthstone, shakes the holy water. Then all make way for Nellie the Juck. Barefoot, she kneels at the new hearth, grips the ends of her shawl in her withered claws, raises them like the wings of a great black bird, and in the ancient tongue intones the spell:

Nellie: 'Aillilliú, a Lú, a Lú,
Beir beatha, beir bú!'
Priest: Through Christ our Lord.
All: Amen.

Dominic Maloney strikes flint, lights a taper, hands it to the old crone. She lights the fire, the first flame leaps up in the dark. Women sob in the silence.

In the leaping light the figure of the teacher is suddenly seen. He has a dark green jacket on, bright buckles on his shoes. To the surprise of all, he has a violin tucked under his chin. His sardonic face is altered, gentler somehow, he draws the bow. At once the floor is cleared. To the leaping strains of the violin in that flickering light, the young men and the girls swing wildly into their barefoot dance.

Long past midnight they troop home through the moonlit wilderness weary and happy. They feel they have made something. They have too. They have made history.

MORE THAN HALF A HUNDRED BOYS, all ages, turned up that first Monday morning. They were all very quiet, nervous. The teacher was there before them in his brown jacket, sitting outside in the shade of the rock, writing at a plank table. One by one they were beckoned up to him, gave him their names, where they lived, and their ages.

The first task was easy. He sent them searching among the pools and the bushes for flat stones, to sit on. They lost their shyness, splashed and laughed. After a while he beat a tin plate with a spoon, called them to order, put them sitting in shady places, in groups according to age. One of the Maloney boys, John, was put in charge of slates. The second boy, Dommy, was sent up on the rock to act as sentry.

This was the most exciting thing. The bigger boys took it in turn, an hour each. The boy on the rock felt important, away above the thatch roof, the little clusters of boys sitting in the hazel shade. The most exciting part of it was, the teacher gave him a pair of wonderful glasses. They moved in and out, with the maker's name written in French. They brought everything close and clear — backyards, children playing in the mud, hens, women feeding pigs — the streak of a hare in the grass, even. You could see carts and cattle on the high road miles off, slow drays of coal or bricks, drovers with sheep, moving up to The Swan, down to Timahoe and Portlaoise, over to Abbeyleix, or down through the trees and the green hedges to the Barrow and Carlow Town. If you saw a Sheriff's Officer, or a Landlord's Agent, or riders in uniform, you were to run down and tell the teacher.

There weren't near enough slates to go round. The teacher broke some in two, so that even the small pets got a piece each. Then Dommy Maloney was sent round with bits of chalk, mostly white, some of it brightly coloured. The teacher banged the plate and ordered everyone not to be putting them in their mouths.

'Here we begin,' he said. 'This is the letter A.' He chalked it on a big slate, and everyone had to chalk it on their own bit. He was very hard, if you chalked it even a slight bit crooked he would make you rub it out with a damp rag and draw it again. He gave a ha'penny to a little pet from Hazel Bog for doing it the best.

When they had learned as far as A, B, C, D,

he put a big book full of coloured pictures on the table, and sliced the pages out with a knife. Everybody watched him, for he was whistling fierce through his teeth as he sliced. Every child got a page. You had to look at it and look at it, and when he came you had to tell him all the things you could see in it. This time it was Mick Leary got the ha'penny. He sent Mick in to light the fire and put on the pot, and sent Patch Cray up on the rock with the glasses hung round his neck in case they'd fall.

Then he sat on the table, gathered them all round him on the grass, and told them a story. 'One winter's night, it was pelting snow, and these shepherds were gathered round a big fire on the hill, keeping the wolf away from their lambs and sheep . . .'

Mick told him his dinner was ready. He said they could all eat their lunches now. Some of the small pets began to cry, they had their bread eaten. But everyone was happy when they discovered that the teacher had a huge pot of potatoes boiled inside in the school, and you got one to cool in your hand, or two if you were lucky. Then they were free to run wild, climb trees, and play Poachers and Jailers, till he banged the tin plate once again.

It was a new game, Numbers. You had to count your eyes, and your ears, and your nose, and legs and arms, and your fingers, and your toes, and draw the number the way the teacher chalked it on the slate. Afterwards, he told them another story, about the Danes, thundering big robbers with horns on their heads breaking up schools and burning the picture-books, until the King gathered up his men and drowned them all in the Sea. Then the teacher took his violin and taught them a song:

> 'Blackbird, blackbird, up on the tree,
> Why don't you learn your A.B.C.?'

The shadows were getting long. Sleepy, they heard him say they could bring home their bits of slate and chalk, and learn their letters and their 1, 2, 3 — but if they lost them, he would put them in the pot and boil them for the dinner!

They saw him go off through the furze with his pack on his back. They noticed he limped a little.

That night there was much talk by the fire-sides.

Mrs. Cray: 'Well, Patch, how did you get on with the Teacher?'

Patch: 'Oh, he's a great gentleman. He has feel-glasses, an' he tells us about fellas with horns on their heads, and he plays the fiddle, and ates his dinner off a plate like a "Prodestung!" '

Enter a Red-head

OWEN'S LITTLE VAN was parked in the shelter of an ivied wall, remains of an ancient Castle. His donkey grazed among the thickets. A painted board on the van read, 'Boots, Leatherwork, Repairs.'

He worked by candlelight, cutting, stitching. In the depth of the night, when silence settled, he would clear a space on the board, take paper and pen out of their hiding-place, draw pictures, print words and easy sentences.

Once a whip-handle banged on his little door. Quickly, he put the school-work out of sight and opened the door, his heart fluttering. A sharp voice called, 'Come here, Cobbler!' A mounted Militia man, brass and leather gleaming in the shaft of candlelight. 'This is it!' thought Owen. But all the man wanted him for was to mend a broken saddle-girth. He tossed him a coin and trotted off into the night. Back at his board, the Cobbler found his hands trembling with anger, with fear.

It was a time of fear. Fear of the knock in the night. It was the time of Culloden, a name that travelled as far as the market-street of Stradbally, into the gravel hills, up into the neck of the Leix woods where Nellie had her shop. And on every ballad singer's lips was the name

— Bonnie Charlie.

The Catholic Prince Charles, claiming to be rightful heir to the Throne, had come from France with a small army and had landed in Scotland. The Protestant Army of England defeated him at Culloden, and began a massacre of his supporters everywhere. The Prince escaped. The ballad-singers sang that he would come again; the Law-makers and the Militia men and the Williamite landlords would be sent to the bogs to cut turf; the Maloneys, Crays, Laceys, Learys, would get back the lands of their fathers; the Williamite churches would be taken over and Catholic bells ring once again in every town.

Owen grinned. He had seen the poor in Catholic France, Flanders, the Belgian cities. Whether Protestant George or Catholic Charlie sat on the Throne, he knew Big Mick Leary would still be skinning rabbits. But there was no arguing with the ballad-singers. He said nothing, plodded on with his A.B.C., Big Eagle is a Red Man; Ten and Ten is Twenty, open yer gob an' ate plenty; Christ before me, Christ behind me, Christ on my left hand, Christ on my right hand; Extent of Time, Extent of Place is expressed in Greek by the Accusative Case; the tide comes thirty miles up the Barrow to St. Mullins; for the Two sides of a Triangle are together greater than a Third; Twelve and Twelve are Twenty-four, go to bed and say no more. And the little voices haunted his dreams.

The Protestants had taken fright everywhere. The Laws were put savagely into force. Bands of Protestant farmers and their followers, armed and uniformed, the Yeomen, the Militia men, rode through the highways and byways, hunting out Priests who had no licence, Popish schoolmasters, old pikes or muskets hidden in thatches, suspicious books, strangers who had come from France or Spain. Often there would be a wild hunting halloo and a gallop by torchlight across fields and boglands, while a thatch flamed and a terrified figure fled for cover among the rocks and furze.

Up the broken stone stairs of the old ruin, Owen had found a little room with a slit window. There he kept his books and papers, his Degree from Douai, his Gold Medal for Wisdom, and the field-glasses from Fontenoy. He closed up the entrance with loose stones. To the great world of the armed and the well-to-do, he was Kelly the Cobbler.

HIS NIGHTS were long and lonesome. By day he was busy, amid the cheerful clamour of his scholars reciting their lessons under the leaves in the wilderness, or inside under the roof if the day were wet. It was hard work, especially with the bigger boys. Most of them were slow, many were scatter-brained; and when the newness of the school had worn off they were inclined to be wild, shouting out of their turn, wrestling with one another when his back was turned, or chucking bits of chalk at the birds. He had to make a leather strap. The Speaker.

The Maloney boys, John and Dommy, were a great help. Their father had taught them to read and write and speak Town English. They were able to take the small boys and teach them the letters, numbers, easy sentences in the picture-pages. Owen started those two at once on Latin Grammar and set them to write out the Wars of Julius Caesar. The Learys, who were rabbit-catchers up in the hills, were vexed at this. Owen had to go up to their village and explain that it was no use trying to teach their Mick Latin till he had learned his letters in English first.

Mick Leary was the wildest and the brightest of all the bunch. He seldom came to school without a rabbit or a hare, sometimes a landlord's pheasant, as a present for the Teacher.

Shillings were scarce, and pennies were not plentiful. There were a few small landowners like the Maloneys who could scrape a few shillings together from the butter and egg-money to pay for the lessons. But the bulk of the men were poor day-labourers, herds, broom-sellers, turf-cutters, dray-men, labourers in the coal-pits, in the brick-pits, in the mills and tanneries down in the Barrow Valley. They earned anything from fourpence to ninepence a day. Out of this they had to pay 'tithes' to the Protestant Rector, and pay for the keep of their own Priest. There was little left for lessons.

On quarter-day, most of the scholars would come to Owen with baskets of potatoes, bags of turf, grey lumps of coal, a handful of eggs, a pair of chickens, a crib of eels. Little things who had nothing to bring would often be found crying in the bushes. Owen quietly taught the bigger boys to give something from their own bags to those who had nothing to bring.

'Now, gentlemen,' he said to them one day, 'write down the first rule in the Science of Wisdom.'

'Da,' ('give'), wrote John Maloney in Latin.

'Don't snare all the rabbits for yourself,' wrote Mick.

Owen looked into the green eyes full of mischief and intelligence. He gave him the Latin Grammar he had brought from Douai. That night the Leary tribe came down from the hills, loaded with game-birds and bottles of home-made whiskey and knocked on the door of the van.

LONGER AND MORE LONESOME the nights grew as the year darkened. At times, waves of anger and boredom would sweep over him, fiddling his life away with these childish lessons, thinking of his days in Europe when he had moved among and argued with learned men. Memories would flood into his mind — the brilliant Catholic services abroad; the deep tone of the Catholic bells not afraid to ring out over the whole City; the great windows with coloured stories pictured in the glass; the forests of books. And the great seaport towns, tongues of all nations to be heard in the streets, news of distant lands, new discoveries, exciting new ideas. And here he was now, hiding in a backward hole of rainy Ireland, trying to teach A.B.C. to the sons of woodmen and rabbit-skinners who thought the world ended at the Bridge of Graigue.

When he could bear it no longer, he would lock the door, hide away his valuable things, and tramp to a crossroads in the woods, to the shop of Nellie the Juck.

The old woman sat warming her shins by the fire. He sat opposite, with paper and pen, writing down her strange Irish talk, while her granddaughter, at a table in the middle of the floor, looked after the 'Shop.'

This was not like the lovely birdlike Irish

he had learned on Kuldy Island. It was a flatter tongue, older somehow, full of odd words and ancient sounds. Nellie had songs, scraps of stories, spells, prayers, curses, handed down from a long-forgotten time. He did his best to spell the sounds that came from her toothless old mouth. Her face was wrinkled and ingrained with the black dirt of those gravel hills. At times he felt as if Laxy's old goatskin book, worm-eaten, was in front of his eyes and speaking.

Murren was 13, big, wild-looking. She had red hair, and dark eyes that looked boldly out of a blaze of freckles. She sold rolls of French tobacco and fistfuls of India tea from a chest hid in the hen-loft, and flounced out barefoot for a bottle of rum or of mountain-whiskey from the store hidden in the straw of the piggery. She did everything in a hurry, poured the drink (called the 'juck') and banged the mug down in front of the customer.

When she was tired she would bang the door shut, let no one else in, and boil tea in a saucepan until it was as black as tar. She filled out mugs of it for the three of them at the fire, poured in a tint of goat's milk and a drop of the 'juck'. The old woman, taking the mug in her claws, always spilled the first sup on the hearth, saying, ' "Sláinte na marbh!" Drink up now, Master. This is what kept me alive this hundred years!'

So the days passed and the nights. He was invited to weddings, at which he used play the violin, and at wakes too. He wrote songs for them of all the local happenings of note, wrote their love-letters, arranged marriage-settlements, engineered causeways across patches of marsh and measured bits of land. He was often asked to write out a defence for a man summoned before the Magistrates for non-payment of tithes, snaring landlord's rabbits, or smuggling snuff or French tobacco up from the Navigation boats. And before the Autumn was out he had stood godfather to half the babies born in the townland of Wolfhill.

Yet he had none of his own kind to speak to, and night after night went back to the loneliness of his little van.

ONE WET MORNING — it was Sowan, the Feast of the Dead — an uncouth figure darkened the schoolhouse door. A man's coat hanging down to dirty ankles dripped mud and water on the floor. The head was swathed in a sodden shawl. A thick red lip was thrust forward as if looking for fight. The whole room roared with laughter.

A fist shot out and took the nearest boy, Patch Cray, a crack under the ear. Boys leaped up everywhere to join in the fight. The master, swiftly taking the Speaker, laid about him right and left. He gripped the wild creature in the coat. The shawl fell off, the red hair flamed — Murren.

'What do you want, child?' he asked.

'Want you to teach me. Like them!'

Again the mocking roar. Facing them in her flame of freckles she spat like a wildcat. He held her back, battered the table with the Speaker for silence.

'So you want to be taught, Murren?'

'Aye. And I'm not asking you to take tick nayther. Here!' She put an arm in her sack and banged a thick bottle of Jamaica rum on the table.

He daren't smile. He called Dommy Maloney, told him to take her down to the back of the room with a slate and teach her the letters. Silence settled. He went on teaching Mick Latin Composition. Many a sidelong glance was cast at the comical sight of a girl at school.

Soon there was a scuffle at the back of the room. Dommy came running, a slate came flying at his head.

Owen stood up, tall, 'Murren!' he thundered.

'The dirty eejit!' she cried. 'He said me letters were wrong!'

He brought her up to the table, put an arm round the damp coat, felt her trembling with passion. 'You'll sit here beside me near the fire.

I'll teach you myself. But throw one more slate in this school and you'll go straight home to your Granny!'

She hung her head. 'I won't so,' she whispered.

She was first at the schoolhouse door next morning. The boys soon got used to her. Without being asked, she took charge of the fire and the dinner-pot, mothered the smallest boys, clouted the bigger, made sure there was enough left in the pot for the teacher. And it was God help any boy, big or small, who left potato-skins on the floor.

Up at the table she tried all Owen's patience. She never ceased asking what's this? and why's that? And she grabbed big John Maloney's Greek book and wanted to read it before she could spell 'cat.' But she was marvellous at Arithmetic, and could do money sums in her head that boys could hardly do on paper.

He set Murren to teach the small boys Tables of Number. But when they made mistakes the names she called them were so bad that some of the parents came up to Owen after Mass and complained.

ONCE A MONTH or so he would yoke the donkey between the shafts of the van, load up with potatoes, eggs, chickens, brogues, harness-leather, and bits of fancy-work, and drive into the Market Square of Stradbally. There among the cattle, the creels of pigs, the cheapjack stalls, he would bargain with all classes, rich and poor alike, for his goods.

Afterwards, he would buy supplies of chalk, ink, paper, and rummage in the shops and stalls for books. They were mostly ragged, covers gone, tuppence apiece or at the most sixpence — 'The Miracles of St. Patrick', 'Life and Adventures of Sweeney the Highway Robber', 'The Tale of a Tub', 'Guide to Bee-Keeping' — anything in print was worth its weight in gold to him. And, remembering Komenius, he picked up every drawing and coloured picture he could lay hands on — ships, racehorses, battles, children being turned into swans, advertisements for Kilkenny Ale, the Duke of Cumberland being thanked by the King for Culloden . . .

He would go to a tavern for a meal and a drink, play his violin and sing for the company, until it was time to yoke the ass and hit the long road home to the ruin before the dangerous dark.

WINTER CAME, and the days were dismal. The turf-fire in the miserable shelter they called a school lit up a few faces only, and they became fewer every day. One morning he found himself all alone at the table, snow sifting by the open door. The utter weariness of his life overcame him; his head sank in his hands. 'Fool,' he muttered, 'fool I was ever to return!'

'Farewell,' he quoted, 'Island of poverty.
I am well quit of your wind and your wave —'

A figure scampered in, shaking snow from a bundle of clothes. Red hair, wet and bedraggled, gleamed in the firelight.

'Good Lord, child, what brings you out on such a morning?'

She answered, gasping. ''Cos I like you, Master. 'Cos you teach me something.'

He walked up and down, not letting on that he was pleased with what she had said. Suddenly, he took a book from his pack. 'Here, young lady, are the Greek letters, the shapes of them and their names. Start learning. Any one that puzzles you, bring it to me.'

She wiped the wet off her hands, tied back her hair. He sat at the other end of the table and began to write out a book for her from memory — the Story of Arion and the Dolphin, the Christmas Story as told by Luke, and sentences from the Passion of St. John.

The New People

FIVE YEARS PASSED. Daily the sentry climbed the rock, and winter to winter the little school under the hazels at Wolfhill hummed on.

The first batch of boys were nearly all of them now out in the world. John Maloney was a Superintendent of Boats for the Navigation Company down the River at Graiguenamanagh. Dommy was in Vienna, in the service of the Archduke. Patch Cray, with hard hat and silver watch-chain, was Clerk of Accounts at the Mills of Millford. Tommy Lowrey of Hazel Bog had started a school of his own near the Rock of Dunamace. Most of the others were clerks, time-keepers, storekeepers, at the Brick Works, Coal Pits, Tanneries, gangers in the Quarries or up in the Forest, boat-masters or mates on the Barrow down from Carlow to Waterford. Mick Leary was in the Irish College at Rome.

But there was no time to be sad. New faces kept coming. He enlarged the little shanty under the rock, built a second room. Here Murren, now a big and bouncing eighteen, acted as his Assistant. She made the picture-books, drew maps and charts, and took on all the beginners.

As the word got round that there was a Master of Greek in the Hills of Leix, travelling scholars began to turn up at Wolfhill. They came tramping with pack on back, often from remote parts of Ireland. The people showed them the greatest kindness — it was known they were studying to get to the Priestly Colleges overseas. Two of them were housed and fed for nothing up at the Leary village.

These youths brought Owen news of the hidden schools. One came from Croom near Limerick, where he had been taught Latin through Irish by the poet, 'The Merry Pedlar', Aindrias Mac Craith. Another had been at the school of Red Donough McNamara near Slieve Gua in Waterford. A tall dark-haired lad with beautiful English had come from a school in a back-lane in Kilkenny City. He took this boy on as his Assistant, at a small wage. For Murren was soon to go. She was to join an Order of Nuns in Waterford.

A big lad hopping on bare feet had come with a bagful of finely written Irish tales. He had been taught in a Furze-School near Kilrush, by Master Seán O Cinnéide, and told how boys were flocking there from Galway and from Clare. Owen loved the lilt of this lad's voice. He was from Clontuskert, in the sandhills beyond the River Suck. There was no teacher at all, he said, in all that country. Yes, he knew Aughrim well. The Cobbler of Aughrim was dead. Perished in a fever that had swept half the townland into a common grave.

IN APRIL, when the primroses were a faint light under the hazels, old Nellie died. The coffin was put on a cart; Owen supported Murren; the women raised a heart-piercing wail in the boreen. The long straggle of funeral went the whole way down to the resting-place of her people, the Fitzgeralds, at Timahoe. That ancient Gaelic tongue was stilled. They buried her in the dark earth, near the great Monastery School of St. Mochua, all in ruins now except for the Round Tower, upthrust sharply against the April sky.

The Priest had a small chapel in Timahoe, thatched and whitewashed, and a cottage beside it with flowers and cabbages. Here Owen brought Murren, pale under the freckles, but with fighting red underlip still thrust out. The old man treated them to wine and biscuits, and wrote out a letter of Recommendation to the Waterford Nuns.

As they left, he detained Owen at the doorway. 'Kelly,' he said, 'you have been good to that fatherless girl.'

'Not at all, Father. Rather, it was she who helped me.'

'I have watched you, Kelly, over the years. Who you are, or where you come from, I have no idea. But I can tell you one thing: you are producing a new race of people in these hills!'

THE SHOP was sold. Murren packed. Saturday, Owen drove her over to Stradbally and bought her a complete outfit, a long black dress with white collarette, and a bonnet with a black lace veil that fell down in front of her face. She laughed when she tried it on. But the laugh ceased suddenly; she broke into a storm of tears.

Sunday, there was a collection at Mass to make up her Dowry for the Convent. Monday, Owen left the school to the Kilkenny boy, drove Murren in his little van to Carlow, in time for the Stage-coach. She let down the veil, clung to him a minute in silence, then lifted her head and stepped aboard.

The long road back. He found she had slipped a little crooked cross into his pocket. He knew it. It had belonged to Nellie the Juck.

THE STARS were paling when he parked by the ruin. Big Mick Leary was waiting for him. 'News, Master,' he said, 'from Rome!' He handed him a couple of packages. 'Piper the Peddler brought them up from a boat at Tinnahinch.'

Candle lit, he read young Mick's letter for the Chief of the Tribe who sweated and smoked and spat in amazement at every sentence. 'Well glory be to the Hand of God, it's himself! It's himself surely, that's speaking across the windy seas to me in every line!'

The other letter, in Latin, was for himself. He felt faint, drank deep from Big Mick's bottle.

Incredible. The signature — 'Philip'. Philip O'Reilly!

The words floated before his eyes — 'We searched high and low . . . My uncle . . . he wrote to everyone he knew in Ireland . . . no trace or tidings of you could be found . . . My uncle sent me to Rome . . . Poor Laxy's Greek took me to the top . . . ordained Priest . . . Doctor of the Sacred Books . . . I lecture at the University . . .' And the message, twice repeated: 'Come to Rome! Letter of Credit, 500 crowns, drawn on my uncle's banking-house in Brussels. Come.'

All the rest of the night tossing on the bed, unable to sleep — Rome! Come to Rome! Doctor of the Sacred Books.

Late next day he rambled across the wilderness to the little school. No sentry. Groups of the big boys playing cards. Most of the younger ones hunting birds' nests. The poor scholar from Kilkenny vainly banging the tin plate with the spoon. Grimly, he took the Speaker in hand. Rome faded in the far distance. He kept them grinding at their books and problems till the sun went down.

That night he hung the little crooked cross above his bed in the van, and wrote to Philip, a humorous letter, in Greek, describing his life. With many thanks for the Credit of 500 crowns. 'Buy me books out of it. Send me the Latin

Poets, Plato's 'Plan of a Republic', and as many copies of Komenius' 'World in Pictures' as you can lay your hands on.'

The Medal for Wisdom

ANOTHER WINTER mired the roads in mud and flooded the marsh-pools right to the school-house door. Another Spring hung the yellow catkins on the hazel trees and brought the bees humming above the tangled hair of the heads bent over their books and slates. And then at last it happened.

Some boys on the way to school had come upon a tramp boiling a can by the roadside. They mocked him, threw stones at his can and ran off jeering when he followed them.

Next day the tramp was in Stradbally, knocking at the backdoor of the Magistrate. He laid information: that there was a Popish school in the wilderness at Wolfhill; that the Master of it let on to be a Cobbler; that his van was parked on the Gracefield road; that he had heard this Cobbler talking in a foreign tongue. The Magistrate gave him a half-a-crown and called out the Militia.

They were all young, hard-riding and reckless men. They armed and mounted, glad of a canter across the country and the chance of a hunt.

They found the van, papers in it, a letter in a foreign language. They heeled the van over into the ditch, set fire to it and struck off into the wilderness, searching among the pools and bushes. Soon a 'Halloo!' brought them spurring from all sides. There lay the thatched shelter against the rock. Inside, rude benches made of boughs, shelves of books, chalked slates, a fire still bright, a pot simmering. Pictures and maps of all sorts fixed to the walls. No roll-books, no list of names. And not a soul to be seen.

They took some books as evidence, set the roof and all the rest ablaze. The Captain ordered them to spread out, comb the countryside for the Cobbler, break down doors if they weren't opened quickly enough. 'And catch some of the young vermin if you can.'

WHEN THE FIRST hint of warning came from the sentry, Owen took nothing but the roll-books. Quite cool, he marched his scholars quickly into the wilderness, circled round behind the Militia, and came to where his van lay burning by the ruin. Up the broken stairs; the stones at the entrance were untouched. He opened up the hole, packed all the children into the little room in the tower, built up the entrance again and kept a watch through the slit window.

At dusk, a red glow in the wilderness told its

tale. Small boys began to whimper with hunger and fear. The moon was up before the clatter of hooves on the road was heard. They passed. The Militia were on their way home for their supper. He set the older scholars in charge, to see all the boys safe home.

Quickly he packed. He took nothing but a heavy coat, his money, the manuscripts he had written down from the lips of Nellie the Juck, his Gold Medal and a couple of books.

By midnight he was at the Coal Pits below The Swan. No place to hide, every cabin would be raided. Dawn found him with blackened face and hands beside the driver on a coal-dray going down to the River.

Three weeks later, the Mate on a coal-barge, in glazed cap and coat with the Company's buttons, limping a little, stepped ashore on the Quays of Waterford, collected his pay at the office, and disappeared into the back-streets of the city.

AS ALWAYS, after the shock of an adventure, he lay for weeks drained of energy. Afraid to stir out, afraid of the faces in the street, the clang of hooves on the cobbles. Sick of life, sick of Ireland, sick of himself even.

'Spring,' he wrote,
'Spring, what a bitter thing it is!
Careless the finch flashes an underwing,

Books burn, thatch flames,
At Wolfhill, well-named.'

His old wound ached. He found the first grey rib in his beard. He was 32, a failure in life, skulking in a rat-ridden attic room. Philip's words kept sounding in his mind: 'Come to Rome!' It would be like coming home. Men and minds of his own kind, the great world of ideas. This was perhaps God's voice calling him. Very well. He would go to Rome.

It was a May morning. He ventured out, heavily cloaked, hat down over his eyes and made his way to the Shipping Office where John Maloney had a friend. Blinded by the deep sunlight, he crossed to the shadowed side. Old shops and stalls, junk of all kinds, a diamond-paned window, books. A name on a yellow sheet caught his eye — 'Goldsmith'. Memories stirred — Lissoy, Quartermaster Byrne, a stupid little boy, a fishing-rod, Nolly they called him. He stopped, looked at the paper broad-sheet — ' "Ballads & Songs", Composed by Mr. Oliver Goldsmith, Scholar of Trinity College, Dublin.' He went into the dark shop, took down the broad-sheet.

Wave after wave of envy flooded over him. Nolly Goldsmith, hardly knew B from a bull's foot, and here he is now, a Poet, his songs in print in a bookshop. His own poems and writings would never get that far but would slowly rot to pieces walled up in a damp ruin. What kind of curse was on him from his birth?

A servant-girl was vigorously sweeping the floor, raising a cloud of dust. It set him coughing. She straightened. Red hair flamed in the murk. She flung the broom from her, threw her arms about his neck.

'Master!'

'Murren!'

As they clung together, a bespectacled figure came from the back of the shop, asking what did the customer want. 'Here you are, Ikey!' she cried. 'Here's your old broom, sweep your old floor yourself! Come on, Master.' She unhooked a gay shawl from a peg, gripped his arm and dragged him out into the street. 'Tell me everything! How's everyone? Big Mick and the Maloneys and the Spiddogue Laceys — and is Milo Byrne into Latin yet — and did you ever get that dummy-boy from The Swan to make a fist of the spelling?'

They were down on the Quays before he could get a word in. He asked what happened? Why she wasn't with the Nuns?

'Arra, they were too stylish for me, Master.' She thrust out the red underlip he knew so well. 'Tea in the morning in bits of china cups you could see through. And all day polishing floors and bits of ornaments. And don't ate, I mean eat, your boiled egg all at the one gulp, Miss Fitzgerald! And crying my heart out all night for Wolfhill.'

They sat in the sun for hours, talking, talking, hardly seeing the boats, the barrels and cargoes thumping on the Quay. He told her of the burning of the school. Swiftly, she put her hand on his, warm and firm. Next moment, he felt himself clutched, the red lips kissed his cheek.

HE PAWNED the Pope's Medal to buy a Wedding-ring. The rest of his money went on a kit of tools, sides of leather, wax, thread, rolls of kip. He bought a donkey and cart from a travelling tin-man and built a little covered roof on it himself.

They spent the honeymoon wandering about the second-hand shops, picking up pots, buckets, bits of bedding, books, reams of writing-paper, chalk, ink, all the pictures they could find. For a Wedding-present she gave him a Book, handwritten by herself: 'The Poems and Ballads of Owen O'Kelly, Master of Arts'.

Buckets and pans rattling, he walking by the donkey's head, she sitting in the doorway of the van holding the reins, they crossed the bridge over the Suir. The road climbed up out of the valley. Looking back, beyond the crowding slates of the City, they saw the Great Ocean shining to the end of the sky. A vessel in full sail lifted and fell like a white bird against the skyline.

'To France,' he told her. 'Flanders. Spain. Or to the Eternal City on its Seven Hills.' He stared long in the distance.

'Never mind,' she said. 'We have our own Hill ahead of us.'

Facing about, they began the long trek to the West. To teach.

Epilogue

ON THE HILL of Aughrim, in the tiny churchyard of Urraghry, they filled in the gravelly grave. The woman, veiled in black, stood by. Two tall young men stood beside her and a red-haired girl clung to her arm.

Among the stones and the grass-mounds, a dense dark throng was gathered. The Priest at the grave's head spoke:

'Good people, you all know where we stand. On this Hill, near one hundred years ago, was fought one of the great battles of history. All the world has heard of it. But of the battle fought here, by this man whom here in earth we lay to rest, the world has not heard. He dies unknown, unhonoured except of ourselves.

'Yet the battle fought by this humble man, in his own humble way, was a greater battle than that other. They fought for political freedom: he fought for the freedom of the mind and the soul of man. They fought with guns, with charging cavalry, and their bones lie scattered in field and bog. He fought with simple chalk and slate, paper and pen; and his scholars are here alive and listening to me; one of them is speaking to you; many are honoured and able in the great Cities of the four corners of the world. He was a Maker of Men.

'For thirty years he laboured here, his good wife beside him, through darkest days of ignorance and despair. And if there is a light of learning at last in this land, you may thank them for it.'

Bowed heads wept in the silence. The woman's strong shoulders stood unmoved.

'God now give him rest. In days to come, his story will be forgotten and his name. But good people, I say unto you, the name of Owen O'Kelly will be written forever in the Book of Life.'

ALL EVENING the people kept dropping into the little cottage with the diamond panes in the village street. The two young men, the mother and the girl, were kept busy pouring drinks, making tea, cutting roast meat.

At last the floor was empty, and they were

alone. She left the loaded tables and work-bench uncleared and packed the three of them off to bed. She sat a long time in the nook by the hearth, under the old shelf of books, staring into the red coals, looking into the years of the past. 'His name,' she thought, 'will not be remembered . . .'

She stood up, a tall woman with a masterful lip. Taking pen and paper to the table, she began rapidly to write: 'The story begins near the village of Aughrim in Co. Galway, where Tadhgeen Kelly, a herd on the land of Archdeacon Trench, had his cabin and family of twelve or fifteen boys and girls . . .'

Grey dawn was at the diamond panes before she had finished the first Chapter.